YOU BE THE JURY

Best Of

Also by
MARVIN MILLER:

You Be the Jury: Courtroom II
You Be the Jury: Courtroom III
You Be the Jury: Courtroom IV
You Be the Detective
You Be the Detective II
Who Dunnit?

YOU BE THE JURY

Best Of

THE JURY

Marvin Miller

Inside illustrations by Bob Roper

SCHOLASTIC INC.
New York Toronto London Auckland Sydney

2   3   4   5   6   7   8   9   10   23   06   05   04   03   02   01   00   99

CONTENTS

The Case of
the Crazy Parrot

LADIES AND GENTLEMEN OF THE JURY:

When a store gives a warranty to its customers, the store must fully stand behind that warranty.

The case you are asked to decide today involves a pet shop. Mrs. Violet Hoffman, the plaintiff, says that the parrot she bought at King's Pet Shop has not lived up to the pet store's warranty. Mr. Tom King, the defendant, disagrees.

Mrs. Hoffman has given the following testimony:

"It was my son Billy's birthday. He's such a good boy, such an intelligent boy, such a creative and curious child, that I wanted to give him an unusual gift. I decided to buy him a pet parrot. I visited several shops before choosing what I thought was the perfect bird. My greatest concern was that I find a parrot that was well behaved."

Tom King, the owner of King's Pet Shop, assured Mrs. Hoffman he had exactly the bird she was looking for. He had trained the parrot himself. Mrs. Hoffman bought the parrot and gave it to her son on his birthday.

1

Billy named the parrot Long John Silver. Long John quickly became a member of the Hoffman family. It spoke out at the most unexpected times and became the center of attention.

One Saturday afternoon, Mrs. Hoffman returned home from the hairdresser. Billy met her at the door with a pained look on his face. When Mrs. Hoffman entered the house, she was horrified to find the living room in disarray. Sofa pillows were strewn on the floor. Books had toppled from the shelves. A large vase had fallen off a table and was lying cracked on the floor.

Long John Silver was sitting quietly, perched on his pedestal.

In tears, Billy told his mother that the parrot had gone berserk. Billy explained that while his mother had been gone, he had been doing his homework. He was typing a school paper when Long John Silver became excited, talking and squawking loudly.

As Billy finished his paper, Long John's squawking suddenly stopped. The parrot jumped off the perch and proceeded to fly wildly around the room. It spread its wings, knocking over everything in reach. When the parrot hit the vase, the crashing sound seemed to make it even crazier. It continued to fly around the room, grabbing pillows in its beak and dropping them as it flew from one place to another.

Billy finally caught the bird and managed to

fasten it to the perch.

Mrs. Hoffman claims that the parrot's behavior violates the pet store's warranty. She not only wants to return the bird but demands payment for the broken vase, which she says was worth $3,000.

EXHIBIT A is the store owner's warranty, found on the bill of sale.

EXHIBIT B is a photograph of the living room where the damage took place. You will note the entire room is in a state of disarray. Fortunately, the only permanent damage was to the vase.

Mr. Tom King, the pet store owner, represents himself as a professional animal trainer with fourteen years' experience. His sworn testimony states:

"I have personally trained hundreds of animals — including dozens of parrots. Remember the movie *The Purple Pirate?* I trained the parrots for all the pirates in that picture. No animal trained by me as a household pet has ever misbehaved in the manner claimed here today."

Mr. King feels strongly about his professional expertise and states the parrot could *not* have done the damage. He believes the damage was caused by someone else, perhaps Billy, and that Billy's story is a cover-up.

Mr. King's attorney has submitted EXHIBIT C as proof of this assertion. It is a blow-up of a section of the photograph in EXHIBIT B. It draws your attention to a boomerang that is lying on a shelf in the room. Mr. King believes the vase could have been easily knocked over by this toy. He states that such a toy does not belong in a living room.

Mr. King suggests that during Mrs. Hoffman's absence, Billy may have been playing with the boomerang and accidentally hit the vase. The other damage was done to cover up the accident and direct blame at the parrot.

Mr. King is willing to take back the parrot. But he flatly refuses to pay for the broken vase, as a matter of principle. His professional reputation has been challenged, and he does not believe that the parrot, which he personally trained, was the cause of the accident.

LADIES AND GENTLEMEN OF THE JURY: You have just heard the Case of the Crazy Parrot. You must decide the merit of Mrs. Hoffman's claim. Be sure to carefully examine the evidence in EXHIBITS A, B, and C.

Should King's Pet Shop pay for the damage? Or is someone else responsible for the damage, possibly Billy Hoffman?

EXHIBIT A

KING'S
PET SHOP
TRAINING WARRANTY

KING'S PET SHOP
TRAINING WARRANTY

King's Pet Shop warrants that birds trained
by the store shall act in accordance with the
behavior and in such manner as normally
expected of birds who have undergone such
training.

EXHIBIT B

EXHIBIT C

8

VERDICT

KING'S PET SHOP
DOES NOT HAVE TO PAY.

Billy claimed he was typing his school paper when the parrot became agitated. Exhibit B shows the living room with his paper in the typewriter.

The typewriter case is nearby. With the case in this position it would have been impossible to move the carriage backward and forward. Billy broke the vase and put the paper in the typewriter to pretend he was doing schoolwork.

The Case of
the Dangerous Golf Ball

LADIES AND GENTLEMEN OF THE JURY:
If you are hit on the head by a golf ball while playing golf, there is very little that you can do legally. When you set foot on a golf course, you accept the risks that may occur. However, if you are standing in your house and are hit on the head by a golf ball, that is quite a different matter.

Such is the case before you today. Jason Compson, the plaintiff, is one of the homeowners of Green Acres Homes. He is suing the developer because a stray golf ball hit him while he was inside his house. Green Acres Development Corporation, the defendant, claims that Mr. Compson's injury is a complete fabrication, designed to harass them.

Mr. Compson has testified as follows:

"My name is Jason Compson. Two years ago, I bought one of the first homes in the Green Acres Housing Development. My home is one of sixty homes surrounding a private nine-hole golf course. Home buyers were invited to join the golf club, which was to be a private recreation center for the housing development."

During its first year, very few people joined the golf club. The club realized it would have to go out of business unless more people joined, so it announced it would change its policies and open the club to the general public.

To accommodate its plans, the club added an additional nine holes, clearing the trees near Mr. Compson's property.

Mr. Compson was upset. When he had purchased his home, he could sit on the patio overlooking the wooded land, barely seeing the golf course in the distance. When the new course was built, trees had been cleared, and he could now see the sixth tee which was fifty yards from his patio.

Before building the new course, Green Acres assured Mr. Compson it would be designed so that all golf shots would point away from his property. But it said nothing about the view. Besides seeing the sixth hole from his patio, Mr. Compson complained that when his windows were open, the constant chatter of golfers could be heard in his house.

Mr. Compson was so angry that he tried to get Green Acres to move the sixth tee. Mr. Compson claimed that the noise of the golfers calling, "caddy!" caused him mental distress, and he was in danger of bodily harm from a stray golf ball.

One day, Mr. Compson's prediction came true.

As he was in his den, hanging an expensive mirror, a golf ball shot through the window, hitting him on the head. He lost his grip and the mirror crashed on the mantle and fell to the floor.

Besides his injury, the mirror was completely shattered. The mantle was also heavily damaged.

Mr. Compson has sued Green Acres for his pain and suffering and for the cost to replace the broken mirror and repair the mantle. He further claims that the accident is proof of the unsafe location of the sixth tee and demands that Green Acres rebuild it farther away from his house.

EXHIBIT A shows the inside of Mr. Compson's den and the broken mirror. From the broken window, you can note the path the ball took directly across from where the mirror was being hung.

EXHIBIT B is a photograph of Mr. Compson, taken two days after the accident. Mr. Compson's lawyer asks you to note the large bandage and dark circles around his eyes. His injury took more than two weeks to heal.

The management of Green Acres presents a different view of the case. They claim that it was impossible for the accident to have occurred. They also state that Compson has repeatedly threatened the management.

A vice-president for Green Acres has testified: "I don't need any photographs or EXHIBIT B's to recognize Compson. I'd know him anywhere by his voice. At least once a day ever since the new course was built, Compson has been telephoning our office complaining about the noise. Compson also complained he would occasionally see a golfer in his backyard, looking for a stray ball and trespassing on his property."

Green Acres posted a guard near Compson's home but was never able to confirm Compson's complaints.

Green Acres argues that Mr. Compson's complaining was staged for the sole purpose of bothering the club. Green Acres offers as proof EXHIBIT C, showing the location of the sixth tee in relation to Compson's house. Because of the direction of the hole, it would be highly unlikely for a golfer to drive the ball into Mr. Compson's window.

Green Acres further claims that Compson had purposely faked the accident, and broke the mirror and mantle himself. They claim that Compson had no witness to the accident.

Green Acres requests the Court to dismiss Compson's charges, and asks that he be stopped from bothering the club and its golfers.

LADIES AND GENTLEMEN OF THE JURY: You have just heard the Case of the Dangerous Golf Ball. You must decide the merit of Jason Compson's claim. Be sure to carefully examine the evidence in EXHIBITS A, B, and C.

Could a golfer on the sixth tee have accidentally driven a ball through Jason Compson's window? Or did he stage the accident to dramatize his unhappiness with the new golf course?

EXHIBIT A

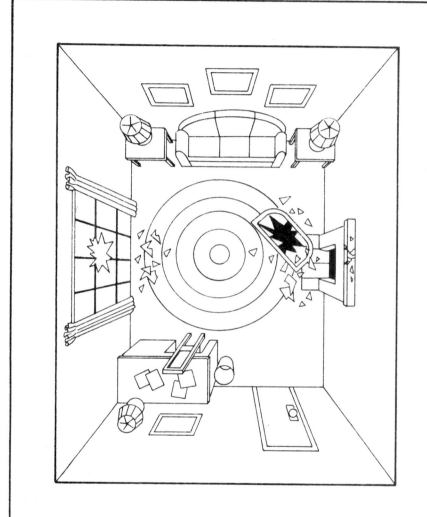

EXHIBIT B

EXHIBIT C

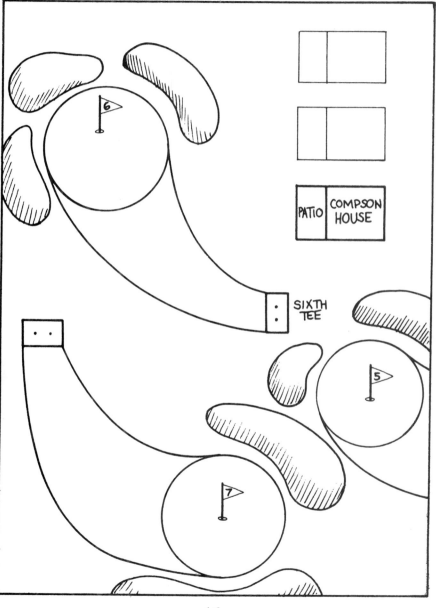

VERDICT

THE ACCIDENT WAS A FAKE.

The accident was faked by Jason Compson. EXHIBIT B shows Compson's forehead covered by a large bandage. If he had been hanging the mirror, his back would have been to the window. The injury would have been to the *back* of his head.

The Case of
The Squashed Scooter

LADIES AND GENTLEMEN OF THE JURY:
If the driver of a car accidentally damages another vehicle that is improperly parked, the driver is not responsible for any damage.

While Archy Leaf, the plaintiff, was shopping at Cherry Hill Mall, his motor scooter was run over by a car driven by Butch Brando, the defendant. Mr. Leaf charges that Mr. Brando purposely ran over the scooter to get even with him. Butch Brando says he is not responsible for the accident and will not pay for the damages.

Archy Leaf has given the following testimony:

"It was Saturday afternoon, July 24. I rode my motor scooter over to the Cherry Hill Mall and parked in an empty parking space. I stopped in at the Card Shoppe for a birthday card for my girl friend. Then I went into Rush Records. My favorite group, Engine Summer, had a new tape out, and I wanted to see if the store had it.

"I remember passing my motor scooter on the way to Rush Records. It was parked upright."

Leaf was in the record store for about five

minutes when he heard a loud crunch and ran outside. To his horror, he saw his scooter lying crushed under the wheels of Butch Brando's car. Several shoppers gathered around the accident, but there were no eyewitnesses.

EXHIBIT A is a map of Cherry Hill Mall with the path Archy Leaf took from the card store to the record shop.

EXHIBIT B is a photograph of the accident scene. You will note the scooter's tangled wreckage under the car.

Archy Leaf continued with his testimony:

"My scooter was properly parked, I'm sure of that. But more important, this was no accident, I can tell you. Butch Brando was out to get me. He's been mad at me for the past two weeks. We both have summer jobs working at Burger Palace. Butch has been coming back from lunch later and later every day, and I finally had to tell the boss. There's too much work for me to handle all by myself.

"The day after I spoke with the boss, Butch came up to me in the parking lot. 'You won't get away with this,' he said. 'I'll get even no matter what. Just wait and see. You'll be *shaking* like a leaf, Leaf, before I'm through with you.' I'm sure Butch Brando ran over my scooter on purpose."

Mr. Leaf seeks payment for damages of $280.00.

Butch Brando has presented a very different version of what happened. I will now read from his testimony. First the question from his attorney and then Mr. Brando's answer:

Q Where were you on the afternoon of Saturday, July 24?

A I was driving around in my car. I love my car. There's no way I would ever do anything that might put a dent in it.

Q When you drove into the mall, what did you see?

A The parking lot was crowded with cars. There were a few motorcycles and scooters parked, but I didn't see Archy's scooter anywhere, if that's what you mean. I finally found a narrow parking space between a van and another car. The van was hogging part of the space.

Q Did you see a motor scooter in that space?

A I certainly did not. At least not from my view behind the wheel. The front of my car sticks out pretty far.

Q Then what happened?

A I drove slowly into the space. All of a sudden I heard something crunch under the wheels of my car. I immediately put on the brakes.

Q How long have you known Archy Leaf?

A Archy and I are old friends. We used to be in Mrs. Kowalski's class back in grade school. He's kind of a nervous little guy, you know what I mean? So I like to tease him, but he knows I'm only kidding. I'd never do anything to hurt him.

Mr. Brando further stated that when he drove his car into the parking space he saw two young boys running away from the scene. He suggests that if the scooter was not carelessly parked flat on the ground by Leaf himself, then the two boys may have knocked it down.

Witnesses have stated that there *were* vandals at the mall at the time, spraying shaving cream across the windows of several cars. Brando offers as proof EXHIBIT C, which is a police complaint by a shopper whose window was sprayed by vandals around the time of this accident.

Butch Brando says that the scooter was lying *flat* on the parking space ground. Since it was parked improperly he was unable to see it. Mr. Brando requests the charges against him be dismissed because the accident was due to Leaf's own carelessness.

LADIES AND GENTLEMEN OF THE JURY: You have just heard the Case of the Squashed Scooter. You must decide the merit of Mr. Leaf's claim. Be sure to carefully examine the evidence in EXHIBITS A, B, and C.

Did Butch Brando knowingly drive his car over Archy Leaf's motor scooter? Or was it an accident?

EXHIBIT A

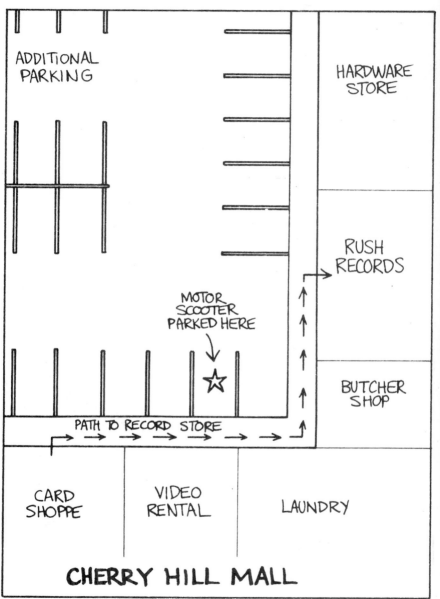

EXHIBIT C

<u>D.D. 5</u>

CRIME CLASSIFICATION	POLICE DEPARTMENT REPORT
VANDALISM	

NAME OF COMPLAINANT	ADDRESS
MS. SANDRA HELFANO	844 Wingate Terrace

11:17 A.M. Complainant was shopping inside

Green's Hardware Store. Claims that two young

boys were creating a disturbance in the parking

lot of the Cherry Hill Mall. She saw them spraying

shaving cream across the windows of cars.

Greg Baldwin

OFFICER ON DUTY

VERDICT

BRANDO SQUASHED
THE SCOOTER ON PURPOSE.

The motor scooter, shown in EXHIBIT B, was crushed under the *rear* wheels of Butch Brando's car. If, as Brando had claimed in his testimony, he stopped the car immediately when he heard the crunch, the motor scooter would have been under the *front* wheels. Brando purposely ran over Leaf's scooter.

The Case of
the High-Kicking Horse

Ladies AND GENTLEMEN OF THE JURY:

If a horse owner does not properly train his horse and it injures someone, the owner is responsible.

Tom Clive, the plaintiff, allegedly was kicked in the head by a horse called Lightning. He suffered severe head injuries and is suing Howard Simm, the owner. He claims that if Lightning had been properly trained, the horse would not have kicked him. Howard Simm, the defendant, says that the horse was well trained.

Tom Clive has testified as follows:

"My name is Tom Clive. I'm a successful jockey who's worked for a number of the top horse owners in the country. I'm the best and I don't care who knows it. Maybe you saw me last year in the Kentucky Derby. Anyway, I was hired by Howard Simm to ride his horse Lightning in the Langdon Races.

"But the first day I was working out with Lightning, Mr. Simm walked up to me and fired me. Just like that! For no reason at all. He told me to get off his property and he'd send me my riding gear the next day.

"Well, I was so angry with Howard Simm that I decided I wasn't going to wait until the next day for my things. I wanted to clear out that night and never see the owner again.

"I snuck back to the stable around midnight. The light in the stable must have been out, so I felt my way to the rear of the stable and over to my locker. I grabbed my gear and headed for the door. Then I remembered I'd left my riding crop inside Lightning's stall.

"When I went to get my riding crop, Lightning was restless and neighing. As I opened the stall door, the horse reared its hind legs and began kicking. He caught me on my forehead. My head still hurts when I think about it.

"I must have been out for hours. When I awoke it was dawn. I could see that Lightning was inside his stall."

Thomas Clive's lawyer entered as EXHIBIT A a photograph of the stall as it appeared that morning.

He also entered as EXHIBIT B a photograph of the baseball hat Thomas Clive was wearing at the time he suffered the injury. Mr. Clive says the horseshoe mark on the hat shows where Lightning kicked him.

In his testimony, Howard Simm raised doubt about Clive's account of the accident. First the question and then his answer:

Q: Why do you question the facts of Tom Clive's story?

A: Well, I didn't like Clive's attitude from the start. I knew he had had trouble with other owners, but I decided to hire him anyway.

Q: What made you change your mind?

A: It was after Clive had his first workout with Lightning. He said my horse wasn't well trained. He called Lightning too wild to be a winner.

Q: Is that when you fired Mr. Clive?

A: Sure. I didn't want a person like him riding Lightning. So I told the jockey he was finished.

Q: What was his reaction?

A: He never expected me to fire him. When I told him I would get another jockey instead, Clive became very angry. He said I would regret it.

Howard Simm offered another explanation for the jockey's injury:

"I don't know why Tom Clive decided to pick up his riding things that night. I told him I'd send them the next day. He might have been trying to hurt Lightning.

"I can't say whether Lightning kicked the jockey or not. But if Clive was stupid enough to go into my stable after dark, he should have known it might be dangerous. Clive could have banged his head on anything. He would have had trouble walking through the stable in the dark."

28

He entered EXHIBIT C, a photograph of Tom Clive's locker, to prove his theory.

"Clive could easily have hit his head on that beam near his locker and used the accident to blame Lightning. He said he would get even with me. Maybe he even faked the whole thing.

"There are old horseshoes inside the barn. If Clive wanted to blame Lightning, all he had to do was find one and slam it into his baseball hat.

"You can't tell from the mark on Tom Clive's hat whether it was done by Lightning or not. Any old horseshoe could have done it."

LADIES AND GENTLEMEN OF THE JURY:
You have just heard the Case of the High-Kicking Horse. You must decide the merit of Tom Clive's claim. Be sure to carefully examine the evidence in EXHIBITS A, B, and C.

Did Lightning kick Tom Clive? Or did the jockey fake the accident?

EXHIBIT A

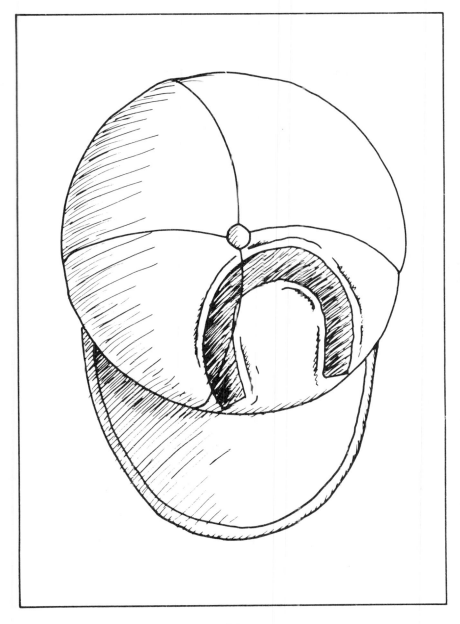

EXHIBIT C

VERDICT

TOM CLIVE FAKED THE HORSESHOE MARK ON HIS HAT.

The mark in EXHIBIT B shows the horseshoe had hit the hat with a downward blow. Clive overlooked the fact that horses kick *upward*. If Lightning had kicked him, the horseshoe mark would have been turned upside down with the round part on the bottom.

The Case
of the Troublesome Twins

Ladies and gentlemen of the jury:

For a person to be found guilty of a crime, there must be sufficient proof that he was the one who committed it.

Keep this in mind as you go over the facts of this very unusual case.

Farmer Foley, the plaintiff, accuses Bart Lee of breaking the lock on his chicken coop door. All the chickens escaped. He is suing Bart Lee for the amount of money it will take to replace the chickens.

Bart Lee, the defendant, claims he is not guilty of the crime since Farmer Foley cannot say for certain whether it was he or his twin brother who did it. If there is not enough evidence to point to either twin, then neither can be found guilty.

Farmer Foley has testified as follows:

"One rainy afternoon, April 19 to be exact, as I was sitting on the porch of my house, I saw a figure sneaking onto the far side of my property. The person was holding something that looked like a large stick.

"As I rose from my rocking chair, I saw the

intruder banging away at the chicken coop door. Seconds later, the vandal pulled the door open and the chickens rushed out, scurrying in all directions."

Farmer Foley chased the intruder through the muddy grounds. As he gained on him, the figure suddenly tripped and fell. When the person picked himself up, Foley grabbed him by the collar and marched him into the house.

The intruder turned out to be a young man of about nineteen years. He refused to identify himself. Despite the youth's pleas, Farmer Foley telephoned the police.

As they waited for the police to arrive, the intruder telephoned his brother and asked that he meet him at police headquarters.

When the police brought the intruder to the station, the young man was permitted to go into the next room to give his keys and money to his brother.

Minutes later, when the young man walked out of the room, the officer booked him for the crime. The youth said his name was Bart Lee, but he claimed he was innocent. And when his brother came out of the next room, he also claimed his innocence. To everyone's surprise, the brothers were identical twins!

While in the next room, the brothers had exchanged some of their clothing. They had purposely confused everyone.

I will now read from the testimony of the arresting officer. First the question and then his answer:

Q: How can you be sure that Bart Lee is the same twin you arrested?

A: Well, he was the first one out of the room. And he was wearing the same striped shirt as the guy I arrested at the farm.

Q: Was he wearing all the same clothing as the person you caught at the farm?

A: No. He had on some of his brother's clothes.

Q: What else was the person you arrested at the farm wearing?

A: I didn't notice everything. But he had on a dark jacket and dark-colored pants when I caught him.

Q: And what about the shirt he was wearing?

A: Yes, he had a striped shirt . I could see part of it under his jacket. And he had on sandals without socks.

The muddy ground around the chicken coop provided an important piece of evidence. This is shown in EXHIBIT A. Whoever broke into the coop left a trail of footprints behind.

EXHIBIT B is one of the sandals worn by the first twin to come out of the room . He identified himself as Bart Lee and is the twin who was booked for the crime. As you will note, an imprint of the sandal Bart was wearing exactly matches the footprints found around the chicken coop.

The arresting officer continued with his testimony as follows:

Q: What happened when you arrived with the vandal at police headquarters?

A: He asked my permission to go into the next room.

Q: Why did you let him?

A: Well, the kid seemed really scared. I figured his brother would quiet him down. But I didn't know that he had a *twin* brother in there.

Q: How long was he in the other room?

A: Only for a few minutes.

Q: Was it enough time for them to switch shirts, pants, and shoes?

A: I don't know.

EXHIBIT C is a photograph of both twins taken at the police station. One is wearing a light jacket and dark pants while the other has a dark jacket and light pants. Both have a shirt underneath. The twin on the left is Bart Lee, the one who was booked for the crime. He is wearing a striped shirt.

The lawyer for Farmer Foley raises an important question:

"Even though the brothers switched some of their clothing, why did the twin who was first to leave the room allow himself to be booked? That is, unless he really is the guilty one?

"Surely common sense argues that the twin who left the room first, and who is on trial here today, has to be the guilty party."

LADIES AND GENTLEMEN OF THE JURY:
You have just heard the Case of the Troublesome Twins. You are to decide the merit of Farmer Foley's accusation. Be sure to carefully examine the evidence in EXHIBITS A, B, C.

Was Bart Lee guilty of breaking open Farmer Foley's chicken coop? Or did his twin brother do it?

EXHIBIT A

EXHIBIT B

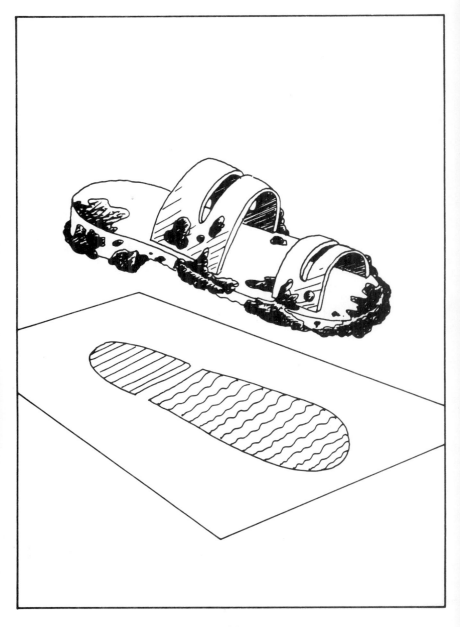

EXHIBIT C

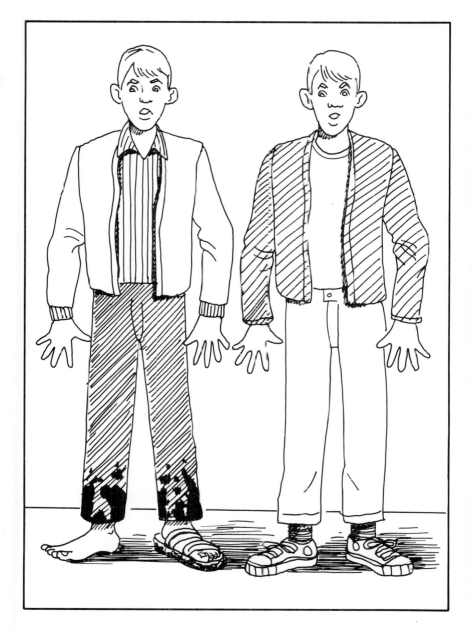

VERDICT

BART LEE WAS INNOCENT. HIS TWIN
BROTHER WAS THE GUILTY ONE.

EXHIBIT B shows the mud-stained sandal that
Bart wore at the police station. But the person
wearing the sandals at the chicken coop would
have his feet filthy with mud. Bart Lee's feet in
EXHIBIT C are perfectly clean.

The clothing Bart Lee exchanged included his
shoes and socks. His twin brother's muddy feet
are inside Bart's socks and sneakers.

The Case of
the Squished Tomatoes

LADIES AND GENTLEMEN OF THE JURY:

If a burglary takes place, and a great deal of money is stolen, the thief may be sent to prison for a very long time.

Carefully consider this serious penalty as you listen to the evidence presented here today.

Since we are in criminal court today, the State is the accuser. The State accuses Andrew Turner, the defendant, of stealing $2,000 from the safe of the Hopp-n-Shop Grocery Store. Andrew Turner, who works at Hopp-n-Shop, insists he is innocent.

The State called Harvey Hopp as its first witness.

"My name is Harvey Hopp. I own the Hopp-n-Shop Grocery Store. On the evening of June 5, at approximately 9:15 P.M., I locked up the store for the night and headed home I learned later that at 9:56 P.M., the burglar alarm for the store's safe went off. Luckily the police responded immediately."

EXHIBIT A is an official record of the burglar alarm report.

When the police arrived, they discovered that

the back door of the store was unlocked. In searching the store, they found the office safe open. The money inside had been stolen.

In a corner of the store, near a vegetable bin, police found a basket of spilled tomatoes.

The thief had left his mark. Damaged tomatoes, some half eaten, were on the floor. On a large wall mirror, scrawled in the juice of a squished tomato, the thief had written the word "DELICIOUS!"

EXHIBIT B is a photograph of the damage done by the thief.

The State questioned Harvey Hopp further. First the question and then his answer:

Q: Are you positive you locked the front and back door of the store on the evening of the burglary?
A: I'm certain I did. I've followed the same routine for years.
Q: Did anyone have the combination to your safe?
A: I'm the only one. But it's possible that someone who worked for me could have seen me open the safe and remembered the combination.
Q: Does anyone else use your office?
A: No. I'm the only one. But sometimes my workers come in if they want to speak with me privately.

Since there was no evidence that the back door

was broken into, police reasoned the burglary was an inside job.

They believed that one of Hopp's workers could have hidden in the store before closing. Then, when the owner locked the store for the night, the thief came out of hiding. He had the store all to himself.

Inside the office wastebasket, near the safe, police discovered a half-eaten sandwich.

The sandwich was sent to the crime lab for examination. A slice of cheese from the sandwich revealed important evidence. There were unusual teeth marks made by the person biting into it.

The police lab report is shown in EXHIBIT C.

The bite marks revealed that the person eating the sandwich had a center tooth missing. It showed the width of his front teeth and the spaces between them.

The teeth marks from the cheese were compared with those of the people who worked in the store. Andrew Turner's teeth marks matched exactly.

His middle tooth is missing and all other teeth matched the marks in the cheese.

On this basis, Andrew Turner was placed under arrest and is on trial here today.

Turner had worked for Mr. Hopp for seven months. But recently there was friction between them. It seemed Turner loved to eat. He constantly nibbled on store food without paying for it.

The State questioned Andrew Turner about his eating habits:

"Food? Sure I love food. Anyone can see that. Just look at the size of my stomach. I love to nibble.

"But I hate tomatoes. I'm allergic to them. Every time I eat a tomato my eyes get watery and I break out in a rash."

The defendant was asked to account for the half-eaten sandwich found in the wastebasket. The following is from his testimony:

"I admit it. That's the sandwich I ate. But I didn't eat it the night of the burglary. I got hungry in the late afternoon. I know Mr. Hopp doesn't like me eating. So I sneaked in his office while he was in the front of the store and gobbled up a fantastic sandwich. When I saw Hopp coming, I tossed the last of it in his wastebasket."

Andrew Turner's lawyer claims that at the time the safe alarm rang, Andrew was at home talking on the telephone to his girlfriend, Nancy King.

Nancy King supported the defendant's story. Miss King said they talked on the phone for about a half hour, although she was not sure of the exact time of the call.

Andrew Turner's lawyer claims that the testimony of Andrew's girlfriend provides the defendant with an alibi. And since Turner is allergic to tomatoes, it is further proof of his innocence.

LADIES AND GENTLEMEN OF THE JURY: You have just heard the Case of the Squished Tomatoes. You must decide the merits of the State's accusation. Be sure to carefully examine the evidence in EXHIBITS A, B, and C.

Did Andrew Turner steal the money from the Hopp-n-Shop's safe? Or was he innocent?

EXHIBIT A

POLICE DEPARTMENT BURGLAR ALARM REPORT	PRECINCT 18th
	REPORT NUMBER 842A

DATE June 5, 1989

TIME 9:56 pm

LOCATION Hopp-n-Shopp Grocery Store
82 Prospect St.

Police car #6 dispatched.

Monique Vespucci

OFFICER ON DUTY

EXHIBIT C

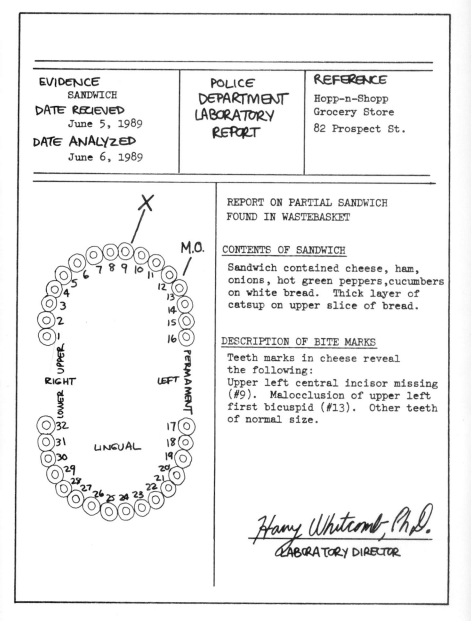

EVIDENCE
SANDWICH
DATE RECIEVED
June 5, 1989
DATE ANALYZED
June 6, 1989

POLICE
DEPARTMENT
LABORATORY
REPORT

REFERENCE
Hopp-n-Shopp
Grocery Store
82 Prospect St.

X

M.O.

REPORT ON PARTIAL SANDWICH
FOUND IN WASTEBASKET

CONTENTS OF SANDWICH
Sandwich contained cheese, ham,
onions, hot green peppers, cucumbers
on white bread. Thick layer of
catsup on upper slice of bread.

DESCRIPTION OF BITE MARKS
Teeth marks in cheese reveal
the following:
Upper left central incisor missing
(#9). Malocclusion of upper left
first bicuspid (#13). Other teeth
of normal size.

Harry Whitcomb, Ph.D.
LABORATORY DIRECTOR

VERDICT

ANDREW TURNER BROKE INTO THE SAFE.

Turner testified that he couldn't be the burglar because he was allergic to tomatoes. In EXHIBIT C, the lab report describes the sandwich Turner was eating. It was topped with *catsup*.

Turner admitted it was his sandwich, but forgot that catsup is made from tomatoes. Andrew Turner really wasn't allergic to tomatoes.

It was Turner who opened the safe and scrawled the sign on the mirror.

The Case of
the Sports Superstar

LADIES AND GENTLEMEN OF THE JURY:

When a person's picture is used in an advertisement without permission, even if that person is a famous public figure, it is an invasion of that person's privacy.

Such is the case before you today.

Byron "Lefty" Ward, the plaintiff, was once the leading pitcher in the National Baseball League. He is suing TV station KBB for illegally using his name and picture to advertise a TV sports event. KBB, the defendant, claims they used Ward's picture with the star's permission.

Wink Hastings of TV station KBB has testified as follows:

"Wink Hastings is my name and TV is my game. I'm the station manager at KBB.

"When KBB got the rights to televise Weston College baseball games, we wanted to attract as many viewers as possible. Then one morning, I got this brilliant idea. They don't call me 'Quick-as-a-

Wink' Hastings for nothing. I realized that if we could hire Byron Ward as our announcer, more people would watch the games."

Hastings met with Ward. The baseball star said he was very interested. Byron Ward signed a letter of agreement stating he would accept the job if the TV station could work out an agreeable contract.

This letter was entered as EXHIBIT A.

During their next meeting, the two men argued over the terms of the agreement. Wink Hastings was under pressure. The day of the first game was approaching. KBB had to begin its advertising campaign.

Byron Ward finally walked out of the talks, stating he had changed his mind. He didn't want to work for KBB. But by that time the advertisement with Ward's picture was in newspapers. It said he was announcing the games.

Byron Ward claims the advertisement damaged his reputation. His fans expected to see him as announcer and they were disappointed.

Byron Ward testified about his dealings with Wink Hastings and KBB. First the question and then his answer:

Q: Is this your signature on the letter?
A: Yes, it is. But Mr. Hastings knew I would announce the games only if he met my terms.

The wording in the letter says so.

Q: Why didn't you take the job?

A: I didn't like Hastings's attitude. First he told me he would pay me a lot of money. Later he changed his mind. I got so disgusted that I told him I didn't want to work for his TV station.

Q: Did you pose for the picture in the ad and give KBB permission to use it?

A: No, I certainly did not.

EXHIBIT B is the advertisement that is the reason for Byron Ward's legal action against KBB. It is a photograph of Byron Ward seated behind a KBB microphone.

Wink Hastings told the court a completely different story:

"When I first suggested the announcing job to Ward, he was very interested.

"I told him we needed to prepare an advertising campaign immediately and he agreed to pose for it. We had his permission.

"But when it got down to details, Ward became unreasonable. Besides wanting a higher salary, he insisted we buy him a new wardrobe. He wanted a different suit for every game. He also said he needed a private dressing room.

"We just couldn't afford his demands. By the time we decided we couldn't work things out, it was too late to stop the advertisement."

Byron Ward states that the station manager is lying. He claims that the picture in the advertisement is a complete fake. He never posed for it.

Ward claims that since KBB needed to prepare the ad before they had a final agreement, someone else posed behind a KBB microphone. Then the artist glued on a photograph of the celebrity's head.

To prove his accusation, Ward explained to the court how he thinks the photograph was made:

"They cut out my head from a photograph taken when I was still playing baseball. Then they glued it onto a photograph of someone else."

Mr. Ward showed the court EXHIBIT C. He believes this is the photograph the artist used to create the picture of him sitting at the mike.

Byron Ward continued his testimony:

"Notice the similarities between my face on the picture in uniform and my face in the ad. KBB eliminated the lock of hair hanging down my forehead. They knew announcers had to have a neater look.

"I never posed for the advertisement. It's an obvious phony, made up from my photograph."

LADIES AND GENTLEMEN OF THE JURY: You have just heard the Case of the Sports

Superstar. You must decide the merits of Mr. Ward's claim. Be sure to carefully examine the evidence in EXHIBITS A, B, and C.

Was the advertisement for KBB prepared with Byron Ward's permission? Or did the TV station use a fake ad?

EXHIBIT A

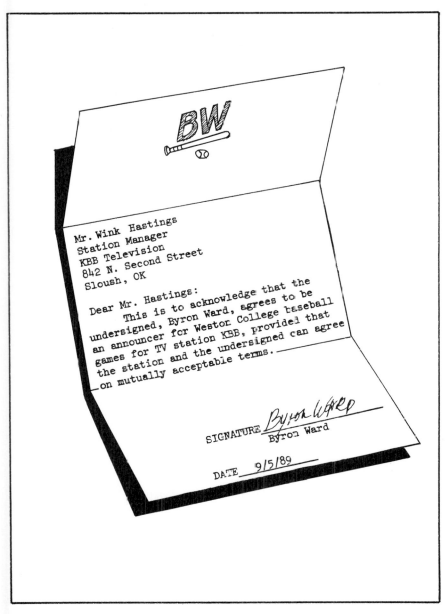

Mr. Wink Hastings
Station Manager
KBB Television
842 N. Second Street
Sloush, OK

Dear Mr. Hastings:

This is to acknowledge that the undersigned, Byron Ward, agrees to be an announcer for Westor College baseball games for TV station KBB, provided that the station and the undersigned can agree on mutually acceptable terms.

SIGNATURE *Byron Ward*
Byron Ward

DATE 9/5/89

EXHIBIT C

09

VERDICT

THE ADVERTISEMENT WAS A FAKE.

EXHIBIT C shows Byron Ward wearing a *left-handed* baseball glove (on his right hand). And Ward's signature on the letter in EXHIBIT A has a slant often seen in the penmanship of left-handed writers. So Byron Ward *was a lefty*.

But the advertisement in EXHIBIT B shows a photo of Ward writing with his *right* hand.

Byron "Lefty" Ward never posed for the ad.

The Case of the Newspaper Photograph

LADIES AND GENTLEMEN OF THE JURY:

If a newspaper reports that a person committed a crime and the article is false, the wronged person can sue. Printing inaccurate information is known as *libel*.

Glen Baxter, the plaintiff, accuses the *Daily Blaze* of falsely printing a news story that said he was arrested for robbery.

Lawyers for the *Daily Blaze* argue that the newspaper should not be blamed for the wrong information.

Mr. Baxter, a shoe store owner, testified as follows:

"Glen Baxter is my name, and I'm very, very upset. Let me tell you how this whole mix-up started.

"I was standing outside my store on Tilgman Street when I heard a woman scream that her purse had been stolen. I turned around and saw her point at a man. He was running the other way.

"I quickly ran after the thief and chased him down the street."

Baxter gained on the suspect. With one swift spurt, he lunged at the thief and wrestled him to the ground.

"After I tackled him, I held his hands tightly behind his back. A large crowd gathered, and I shouted for someone to call the police."

A nearby police car answered the call. A policeman broke through the crowd and arrested the thief. As Mr. Baxter handed him over, a flash went off at the rear of the crowd. A reporter for the *Daily Blaze* had taken a picture of the arrest.

Glen Baxter continued his testimony:

"Other policemen arrived. I didn't want to be involved. As soon as the purse snatcher was arrested, I quickly slipped into the crowd."

The next day, when the plaintiff read a report of the robbery in the *Daily Blaze*, he was shocked to see a picture of himself standing with the thief and the arresting policeman. But the caption under the picture wrongly identified Glen Baxter as the purse snatcher.

EXHIBIT A is the newspaper article that reported the arrest. Baxter, wearing a white shirt, is described as the thief.

Mr. Baxter claims that the *Daily Blaze*'s mistake caused a loss of business for his shoe store.

"I moved to this town about a year ago. After

I bought the store, business started to improve. But when the picture appeared, customers started avoiding me. They began shopping at another shoe store downtown."

Glen Baxter is suing the *Daily Blaze* for his lost business and for damaging his reputation. Even though the newspaper printed a correction, many people never read it. They still think of him as a thief.

Walter Tubb, a reporter for the *Daily Blaze*, took the stand.

"This is all a terrible mistake. I was the one who took the picture. But it was a policeman who gave me the wrong information. The police are the ones to blame, not my newspaper."

Mr. Tubb testified as follows. First the question and then his answer:

Q: Did you write the caption under the picture?
A: Sure, I admit to it. But I got the information from a policeman at the crime scene. I wrote the picture's caption from my notes.
Q: What did the policeman say?
A: He told me about the robbery and that the person standing on the arresting policeman's right had stolen a lady's purse. The other man on the policeman's left had caught him.

The thief was later identified as Harry Hooper.

He is a known criminal with a prior history of petty theft. Hooper's police record appears as EXHIBIT B.

Walter Tubb's questioning continued:

Q: Could you have been mistaken? Is it possible that in the confusion you wrote down the wrong information?

A: Absolutely not. I'm certain of it. I'm positive I was told that the robber was standing on the policeman's right.

Q: What was the name of the officer who gave you the information?

A: I don't know. With everything going on, I never had time to ask him. I don't think I'd recognize him.

Q: Didn't you see Mr. Baxter leave the crime scene and slip into the crowd after the arrest? Couldn't you have figured out he wasn't the thief?

A: I went back to my office right after I took the picture. I never saw Baxter leave.

Lawyers for the *Daily Blaze* presented EXHIBIT C, a page from Walter Tubb's notebook. It shows how he clearly marked the people in the photograph he had taken. He used these notes to write the caption under the picture.

The *Daily Blaze* argues that the Police Department is to blame. They say that the notes in

Walter Tubb's notebook were copied down directly from a policeman's statement.

Their newspaper has a reputation for being careful, not careless. They ask that the charges against the newspaper be dismissed.

LADIES AND GENTLEMEN OF THE JURY:
You have just heard the Case of the Newspaper Photograph. You must decide the merits of Glen Baxter's claim. Be sure to carefully examine the evidence in EXHIBITS A, B, and C.

Did a policeman give the *Daily Blaze* wrong information? Or was the newspaper at fault?

EXHIBIT A

PURSE SNATCHER ARRESTED

YESTERDAY AFTERNOON, A SUSPECT WAS APPREHENDED WHILE STEALING A WOMAN'S PURSE OUTSIDE STAR'S DEPT. STORE. THE ALLEGED THIEF IS SHOWN ABOVE IN A WHITE SHIRT ON THE ARRESTING POLICEMAN'S RIGHT. HE WAS WRESTLED TO THE GROUND BY THE UNIDENTIFIED MAN ON THE POLICEMAN'S LEFT.

EXHIBIT C

VERDICT

THE *DAILY BLAZE* WAS AT FAULT.

The window sign of Star's Department Store in EXHIBIT A has backward lettering. And the thief's scar is on his left cheek, while in EXHIBIT B it is on his right cheek. This means that the newspaper had printed the picture in *reverse*!

In developing the photograph, the negative was accidentally turned over. Everything in the picture was reversed. The person on the policeman's right was pictured on his left and vice versa.

When the reporter wrote the picture caption from his notes shown in EXHIBIT C, he didn't realize the mistake.

The Case of the
Thirsty Helper

LADIES AND GENTLEMEN OF THE JURY:

When a person is hired to work by the hour, she or he is expected to do the job responsibly. Otherwise, the employer does not have to pay in full.

Consider this as you listen to both sides of the case presented to you today.

Donald Breen, the plaintiff, says he overpaid a woman he hired to work for him. She only did half as much work as she should have. But Emily Chowder, the defendant, disagrees.

Mr. Breen recently purchased an old motel located on a main highway. He fixed up the rooms so they looked brand new. A week before the motel opened, Breen planned to send out announcements.

Mr. Breen hired Emily Chowder to help with the mailing. Her job was to take 1,000 announcements, fold and stuff them into envelopes, and paste on stamps.

The two agreed that Emily would be paid $6.00 an hour for the job.

The plaintiff explained to the court why he is suing Emily Chowder:

"It was about eight o'clock in the morning when Miss Chowder arrived at my motel office. She was ready to start the job. I left her alone at the desk while I ran some errands.

"When I got back later that afternoon, Miss Chowder was still at the desk, folding the letters and stuffing them in envelopes. She had finished only half the job.

"The woman said she had been working for eight hours straight. I was surprised she hadn't finished. But I paid her for the eight hours anyway and said I would finish the rest of the job myself."

EXHIBIT A is a photo of Emily Chowder at the desk when Donald Breen returned. Notice the piles of announcements that still need to be stuffed into envelopes.

Mr. Breen continued his testimony.

"I couldn't understand what took her so long until I noticed that the rear door to the office was open. It leads to my motel's swimming pool.

"Suddenly I realized why Miss Chowder had finished only half the job. There, by the edge of the pool, I saw puddles of water.

"Emily Chowder wasn't just stuffing envelopes all day. She did some goofing off, diving and swimming in the pool. The fresh puddles of water prove it."

EXHIBIT B is a photograph of the deep end of the pool where Donald Breen saw the puddles.

Breen was very upset. He timed himself while he stuffed the remaining 500 envelopes. He finished the job in four hours. It had taken Emily eight hours to do the first 500 envelopes.

Mr. Breen is suing to recover the extra money he paid her. He says he should pay the woman only for four hours of work.

Emily Chowder took the stand and described her work to the court. She insisted it really took her the full eight hours.

"I'm a very particular person, you know. I figured Mr. Breen wanted me to do a very neat job, so I was very careful. I neatly folded each announcement before I inserted it.

"Mr. Breen didn't even have a moistener for me. I had to lick the envelopes with my tongue. That took extra time. And the glue tasted just terrible."

Emily Chowder explained to the court why she feels that Breen is mistaken. First the question and then her answer:

Q: Why did Mr. Breen finish the job much faster than you?

A: I think he was trying to prove I was too slow

so he could get some of his money back. I could have done the job a lot faster, too. But it wouldn't have been very neat.

Q: Did you take any time off during the eight hours?

A: No, I didn't even eat lunch. I worked straight through without stopping.

Q: Then how do you account for the puddles around the pool?

A: It's all because I had to lick those envelopes shut. I stopped each time I got real thirsty. My tongue and throat became very dry.

Miss Chowder claimed that she looked around for a water fountain, but couldn't find one. Then she went outside by the pool and found a hose.

Miss Chowder turned on the water several times during the day to drink from the hose. But the last time, just before Mr. Breen returned, she had an accident.

"As I was drinking from the hose, Mr. Breen's dog came running toward me. It knocked the hose right out of my hand. The water sprayed everywhere.

"The water came out so fast that the hose kept on whipping back and forth. When I turned off the water, the whole area was drenched."

The defendant offered as evidence EXHIBIT C. It shows the hose she drank from which was near the motel pool.

Emily Chowder claims that she never swam in Donald Breen's pool. She worked nonstop, except when she got thirsty. She says she is entitled to keep all the money for her eight hours of work.

LADIES AND GENTLEMEN OF THE JURY: You have just heard the Case of the Thirsty Helper. You must decide the merits of Donald Breen's claim. Be sure to carefully examine the evidence in EXHIBITS A, B, and C.

Did Emily Chowder do a full eight hours work? Or did she take time off to go swimming?

EXHIBIT A

EXHIBIT B

EXHIBIT C

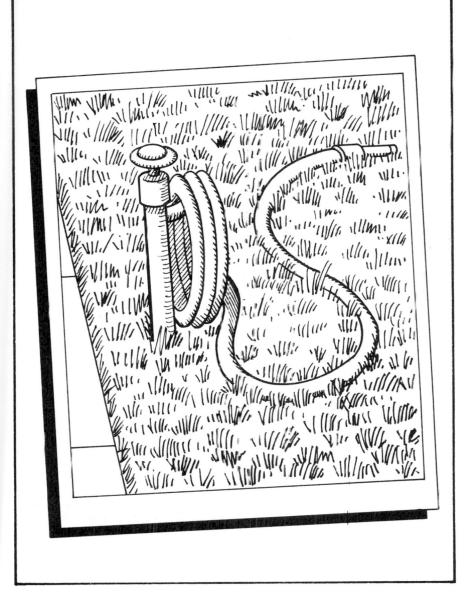

VERDICT

EMILY CHOWDER NEVER WENT INTO THE POOL.

Had Emily swam in the pool, her hair would have been soaked, too. She couldn't possibly have had the neatly styled hair shown in EXHIBIT A.

The Case of the Counterfeit Shopper

LADIES AND GENTLEMEN OF THE JURY:

Distributing fake money is a criminal offense. It is punishable by a long jail sentence.

The federal government, represented by the district attorney, has charged Gilbert Nelson with buying merchandise using counterfeit money.

Mr. Nelson, the defendant, claims he is innocent. He says that it was another shopper who passed the counterfeit bills.

A security guard for Appleby's Department Store was called to the stand:

"My name is Jed Archer, and I have been a security guard with Appleby's for twenty-four years.

"I was at my station on the second floor when Rhonda, the cashier in the coat department, frantically waved in my direction.

"She showed me seven $10 bills that a customer had just given her. He had used them to buy a raincoat. She said the bills seemed funny.

"I examined them closely. They were all brand-new and looked real. But when I ran my thumb across their faces, they just didn't feel right."

EXHIBIT A is a close-up photograph of one of the $10 bills. A crime laboratory has identified it as counterfeit. Note how it compares with a genuine $10 bill. Lines on the outer margin and scroll of the fake bill are blurred and uneven.

Mr. Archer continued his testimony:

"Rhonda pointed across the floor at the man who had just given her the money. He was walking toward the down escalator. I yelled for him to stop. When he heard my voice, the man broke through the crowd and began to run.

"Appleby's Department Store has a steep escalator leading from the second floor to the main floor below. I had to think fast. I pushed the escalator button and switched the stairs so they moved upwards, in the opposite direction.

"Switching the direction of the escalator was a great idea. But the shopper was too quick. He ran down the steps faster than the escalator steps moved up. I chased, but couldn't catch him.

"By the time I was halfway down the steps, the counterfeiter had reached the main floor. He darted out the front door."

The security guard stopped the escalator and telephoned the police.

When officers arrived, they examined the area. A man's wallet was discovered on an escalator step.

EXHIBIT B shows where the wallet was found. An "X" marks the spot. The police believe it was dropped by the criminal during his escape.

Credit cards inside the wallet identified its owner. The wallet belonged to Gilbert Nelson. On this basis, Nelson was arrested. He is charged here today with passing counterfeit money.

Mr. Nelson states that the wallet is his, but he was not involved in the crime. He testified as follows:

"I'm innocent! Sure, I was shopping in Appleby's Department Store that afternoon. But I was nowhere near the coat department.

"There was a lot of yelling going on, and I saw it all happening. I heard the guard shout and run down the escalator. In fact, everyone in the store stopped to see what was going on."

Gilbert Nelson was questioned by the district attorney:

Q: How did your wallet get on the escalator steps?

A: It must have fallen out of my back pocket when I walked down the escalator. But that was after the counterfeiter fled. I left the department store about ten minutes later.

Q: The security guard testified that he stopped the escalator after the criminal escaped. The steps weren't moving. Why didn't you take an elevator instead of walking down the escalator?

A: It might have been easier, but it would have been slower. I was in a hurry. There were long lines at the elevators.

Q: Exactly where were you shopping?

A: I was at the necktie counter on the second floor. I never went near the coat department.

Q: Then how do you account for the counterfeit $10 bills in your wallet?

A: They must have been given to me as change by the clerk at the necktie counter. I remember giving her a $50 bill. The tie cost $9.95. She gave me change of a nickel and four $10 bills.

EXHIBIT C is Gilbert Nelson's wallet, discovered on the escalator steps. The four $10 bills in it have been shown to be counterfeit.

Mr. Nelson's lawyer claims that the counterfeiter could have used fake bills at the necktie counter first, before shopping in the coat department.

These were the counterfeit bills that the necktie clerk took from her cash register and gave to Gilbert Nelson as change.

LADIES AND GENTLEMEN OF THE JURY:
You have just heard the Case of the Counterfeit Shopper. You must decide the merits of the

district attorney's accusation. Be sure to carefully examine the evidence in EXHIBITS A, B, and C.

Was Gilbert Nelson the man who passed the fake bills? Or was he mistaken for the counterfeiter?

EXHIBIT C

VERDICT

GILBERT NELSON WAS INNOCENT.

While the counterfeiter was fleeing, the escalator was switched so the steps moved upwards.

If it had been the criminal's wallet that had dropped, the escalator would have carried it to the *top* step.

EXHIBIT B shows where Gilbert's wallet was found. It is on the *bottom* step of the escalator. This means Gilbert had walked down the steps after the counterfeiter had fled and the escalator was stopped.